# The Taming of
# WILD RICE

## By Harold Kosbau

For more information,
email harold@tamingofwildrice.com

ISBN 0-9774652-0-9


Book Design and typesetting: Treasure Bay Printing
Cover Design: Treasure Bay Printing


Printed in the United States of America


First Printing: October 2005

09   08   07   06   05      5   4   3   2   1

806 NE 4th Street
Grand Rapids, Minnesota 55744
(218) 326-3466
www.TreasureBayPrinting.com


To order email  *harold@tamingofwildrice.com*
Reseller discounts available.

# Index

# Preface

This is an effort to preserve the history of the domestication of wild rice from a native lake crop to a cultivated farm crop. The prompting of my wife, who has reinforced me through "thick and thin", and urged me to capture my knowledge for future generations; and as I surveyed the information on wild rice for the grandchildren, I realized the large accumulation of pictures and articles I had on people, events and research in the evolution of a new farm industry. So the wheels started turning in my brain and the memories were flashing back of all the events I had witnessed, and here I am putting it down on paper.

With the memories came the relationships I have had with the people who had visions, ambitions and courage to launch their careers into this new frontier of developing a new grain crop that would thrive in our unproductive Minnesota wetlands. These are the people and the events I will try to portray fairly and accurately as I write this manuscript.

This history of wild rice is dedicated to my brother, Franklin, who was the real pioneer and leader in the early stages of how this crop could be transferred from a "wild" non-tamable crop to a manageable farm cultivated crop.

I also dedicate it to my son, Hal, who worked on our farm during the summer months and weekends under the guidance of his uncle and acquired a love and curiosity for growing this new crop, as well as the other grain crops.

 His zest for more scientific knowledge in growing crops led him to attend the University of Minnesota and earn a Bachelor's degree in Soil Science. Hal came back to the farm to practice his knowledge, but at age 28 he lost a gallant battle with cancer. He lived his Christian faith to the end, and has passed the "torch" to his son, Nathan, who is following his footsteps.

My beloved grandchildren have inspired me with their curiosity and their desire to know more about wild rice. Like my children, wild rice is a favorite subject for school papers, and their teachers soon know they have "connections" to the wild rice industry. They have ridden on and helped me operate tractors and combines since they were 2 years old and asked a million questions, but I enjoyed every minute. They are Nathan Kosbau, Joseph Doyle and Jena Doyle.

I am grateful to the pioneers in this industry who persevered through the many trials of a new adventure, including the farmers, processors, marketers, the Minnesota Paddy Wild Rice Council, the International Wild Rice Association, and the on-going research program of the University of Minnesota, USDA, and others.

A special tribute to my wife, Betty, who has supported and sustained my efforts to earn my college degrees, move from town to town in search of better teaching positions, and then to abandon this security to enter into the "unknown" in search of ways to domesticate a wild crop. Betty's support throughout our 49 years of married life, along with our united Christian faith, has provided the strength and base to sustain us through "thick and thin".

# Staple Food
## of the
# Native Americans

Climate of the North-Central region of North America was conducive to the growing of an aquatic grass. This grass produced a seed, which was edible for wildlife and humans. The name given to it by the Native Americans was *"Manomin,"* meaning food or good berry, and the name Menomonee in Ojibwe means "wild rice gatherers."

The main areas where it grew naturally were in the States of Minnesota, Wisconsin, and Michigan; and the Canadian Provinces of Ontario and Manitoba. It grew mainly in the shallow areas of lakes and rivers that had a fresh supply of water to provide oxygen and nutrients to the plants.

Native Americans in this area would harvest the seed with canoes using push poles and knockers. The knockers were two pointed cedar sticks about 3 ft. long. One was used to pull the wild rice head over the canoe and the other to tap the head and dislodge the mature kernels. The seed had to be dried and the hulls removed before it could be used as human food. They would either spread the seed out to dry, or heat it in a container over a fire and stir it with a canoe paddle to prevent burning. This later method was most widely used as it reduced the moisture for long-term storage, gave it a roasted flavor, and made the hulls dry and easy to remove from the kernel. Heat from this drying would often cause the kernel to puff open and cause the seed to cook faster. To remove the hulls they would make a pit, line it with leather skin, and place a pole on either side of the pit to hold on to for balance. They would wrap their feet and legs with leather, place the hot roasted wild rice in the pit, and do a twisting "dancing" movement to loosen the hulls. After the hulls were loosened, the wild rice and hulls would be placed in a winnowing basket made of birch-bark, and tossed into the air so that the lighter non-wild rice materials could be blown away from the kernels. After this processing the high-moisture, perishable seed was now dry and storable. It was placed in birch bark containers and stored for use during the long, cold winter months. Containers have been discovered in the Mille Lacs, Minnesota, area that had been buried for many years and the wild rice was still edible.

Wild rice was highly valued as a very nutritious staple food by the Native Americans. Wars were fought for control of the areas where an abundance of wild rice could be harvested. Besides being a food supply, it was used for trading with the French and British explorers and traders. This new grain to the Europeans was called "wild oats, wild rye, or wild rice." The name "wild rice" seemed to fit and continued to be used due to the plant being grown in water like the white rice. There are not many other similarities though as wild rice is an aquatic grass.

In the late summer weeks of August and September the seed matured to a black, long, firm kernel and is easily dislodged, known as shattering, by a wind, rain or the brush of a knocker by a harvester. If wind or rain loosened the seed, it would fall into the water where it was food for the waterfowl or seed for the next year's crop. The seed has a water-impermeable bran layer, which preserves the viability of the seed until it has gone through a cold period. The freezing of Northern lakes provides this cold that breaks the seal and prepares the seed to grow when the warming of the waters comes in the spring.

This abundance of seed that had fallen in the shallow waters provided nutrients for fat and strength needed by waterfowl preparing for the long flight to the southern states. The large local population and the Canadian raised flights of ducks and geese would congregate in the wild rice areas during the fall. This concentration of waterfowl would attract the Native Americans and other hunters to hunt the ducks and geese. The waterfowl and wild rice that had been a festive and staple food for the Native Americans became a Holiday delicacy of the new settlers and in the fancy restaurants.

The use of wild rice for bartering by the Native Americans acquainted the white settlers to the unique, tasteful, nut-like, roasted flavor. It enhanced the flavor of meats, waterfowl, birds, fish, grain and vegetables with which it was cooked. Demand for wild rice increased as it was introduced to people living outside the production area.

Marketers perceived the profitability of buying from Native Americans and white harvesters, and marketing to stores and restaurants in the more densely populated cities. The improvements in transportation and communication in the 1930's and years following promoted the introduction of wild rice to new users. The fancy restaurants catering to rich tastes of customers, the specialty shops featuring higher value food items for gifts or the distinctive appetite, and the grocery stores featuring new products became attractive markets for these enterprisers.

Competition developed for the supply of this new rare commodity. The annual production was not stable. It fluctuated with the patterns of weather, which affected the crop during the growing and harvest seasons. Too much or too little rain, heavy winds, hail, an early frost, or a large population of rice worm, were all factors that influenced the quantity and quality of the crop. On an average there was a real good crop one out of four years. During the lean years there was not enough to supply the local needs, much less the new expanding markets. The quantities of the total lake rice crop ranged from a couple hundred thousand pounds in the lean years to one million or more in the good years. The need for a supply for the new markets caused the marketers to become aggressive in buying during the short years.

The harvest of the natural crop was regulated by the Department of Natural Resources in Minnesota and the Canadian Provinces. Native Americans had exclusive rights to harvest wild rice on lakes within the Reservations. Caucasians had to purchase a license and abide by the regulations controlling the size of canoes and harvest sticks. The date to start the harvest coinciding with the maturity of the wild rice, and time of day to start and cease harvesting. It was not easy to determine a date that was the right maturity date for all of the lakes because of the influences of daylight, temperatures and water levels on the growth of the wild rice plants--maturity dates could vary two weeks from one area to another area, especially north to south.

The method of harvest in the natural stands is shown in Pic. 1. Two people were involved with one standing in the canoe with a long, forked push pole pushing the canoe through the dense stands of wild rice in shallow waters; while the other person sat in the canoe pulling the plants over the open canoe with one "knocker" while brushing the heads with another "knocker" stick to dislodge the mature grain. The two sticks are about 3 ft. long each, tapered, and usually made of cedar. The harvest would commence when it was determined that there were enough mature wild rice kernels per head to justify disturbing the crop. The "beating" of the heads was gentle enough to dislodge the mature kernels without disturbing the immature kernels. Some of the Native American harvesters would tie the green plants together for stability so the wind would not move the plant and heads so violently that the kernels would fall into the water. After the first harvest, a big celebration was held and a feast prepared of the new grain. A good harvest would mean that there was food for the upcoming cold winter.

Pic. 1 Man pushing, woman harvesting

The following pictures are of how the green wild rice was roasted in a kettle and stirred with a canoe paddle, Pic. 2. The roasting of the wild rice caused the hull to become brittle and fragmented. The hot, dried wild rice was now placed in a hide-lined hole or kettle and "danced" on until the hulls were completely loosened from the kernels, Pic. 3 and 4. Then the grain and chaff had to be separated. The mixture would be placed in a birch bark container and tossed into the air to allow the wind to carry away the lighter hulls and plant material, Pic. 5. Now the wild rice was ready to eat and store. Extra wild rice, beyond what the families will need for their own use, will be traded with the local merchants for necessities, or sold for currency.

Pic. 2 Roasting over fire and stirring with canoe paddle

Pic. 3 "Jigging" or "dancing" on hot wild rice rice using push pole for support.

Pic. 4 "Jigging" with leather wrapped around feet and legs.

Pic. 5 "Winnowing" cleaning the wild rice.

This method of harvesting and processing wild rice by the Native Americans has not changed since their ancestors used wild rice as a staple food for their survival. They value the taste developed by the heavy roast, the quick cooking caused by the "popping" of the kernels due to hot temperatures, the lighter color due to immediate roasting and not aging and maturing the kernels, and the non-mechanized process of the way the whole process is done.

Each band of Native Americans had exclusive possession of the wild rice harvesting on lakes within an area near where they lived. No person outside this band was allowed to harvest on these lakes. Some of the bands had special types of wild rice, which were sought after by the buyers and public. Nett Lake, south and west of Orr, MN, was one of those bands with special wild rice. The wild rice kernels were twice as thick as kernels from other lakes and had a distinctive taste. Nett Lake was not a large lake compared to Mille Lacs Lake. The whole lake was shallow and was capable of having a crop which would exceed one million pounds. Buyers would compete very vigorously in order to have the right to purchase this crop of wild rice. The band of Native Americans who possessed Nett Lake was relatively small in number. In the 1970"s and 1980's there was a dispute between families in this band and they divided up with different leadership. This dispute was so severe that an agreement could not be reached on when to harvest and the sale of the crop; as a result, the crop was not harvested. As time went on and there was no settlement of the dispute, the anger led to the shooting and death of some members of a family. This caused a big shakeup and the laws of the Federal Government had to be imposed. The violators stood trial and received prison sentences. An election was held and new leadership was elected.

At East Rice Lake, south of McGregor, MN, another small band had a unique wild rice that was sold green, unprocessed, at an auction. Due to the good quality of this wild rice and it being sold in a lot of 20,000 lbs. or more, there was a fairly large crowd of buyers for the auction. The competition for this lot of wild rice and the competitive bidding at the auction usually made this wild rice the highest priced green wild rice in the whole industry.

These two bands of Native Americans sold their excess green and it was processed by whoever purchased it. They processed the wild rice needed for their own use in the traditional way as described in Pic. 2 to 4. Other bands kept their wild rice and traded or sold packaged wild rice under the Native American Hand-harvested label, usually at a price double the price of paddy wild rice. The justification for the higher price is scarcity, appeal to some consumers for organically grown crops, the different highly roasted taste, and the shorter cooking time.

As long as traditions of the Native Americans are passed on from generation to generation, the excitement and fulfillment of the "wild rice harvest" will be a highlight of the year. There is an effort being made by the elders and leaders to maintain and continue the relationship they have had with this wild crop that has sustained their ancestors.

There is a concern among some of the Native American leaders that the "cultivated" wild rice is a threat to the markets for their wild rice. There may have been some competition when wild rice was first being "paddy" grown, but new markets developed for the farm grown wild rice in the commercial markets which demanded secure and larger quantities to fill their needs.

The pictures of Native Americans came from the Minnesota Wild Rice Council and various news publications, which can no longer be identified. My appreciation to those unnamed who are in the pictures.

# Wild Rice is Tamed

The distinctive, nutty-like roasted flavor of wild rice was appealing to the people who were being introduced to it in the white-linen tablecloth restaurants. It was being served with fowl, meats and fish, in dressings and side dishes. A growing demand for wild rice placed pressures on the cyclical production and unreliable supplies, and caused the prices to go exceedingly high.

Nature was the major cause of a cycle of one bumper crop of wild rice followed by two to four years of lean crops. The poor crops were a result of several factors: 1) The shattering of grain into the lake waters during an abundant crop year provided too much seed for the following year and a plant population too dense to allow healthy plant growth. 2) Excessive rainfall during the early growing stages of the wild rice plant when the plant roots were short and the buoyant plant leaves were on the water surface, along with winds and wave actions, caused the plants to become uprooted and float to shore. 3) A shortage of rainfall lowered the water levels in the lakes and dried up the shallow areas depriving the wild rice of the water needed for early plant growth. 4) A heavy infestation of the wild rice worm, which eats the seed; or a large concentration of blackbirds, which eat the seed, and worms while they shatter large amounts of the grain as they perch on the head and fly from plant to plant. 5) An early severe frost when the plants are immature stops the growth and the plants die. 6) Storms with high winds, rain and hail during the late stages of plant development will shatter any mature wild rice and may destroy the plants completely. 7) As a natural Native American and public owned crop, there was little control over these factors, which affected the production of wild rice.

In the early 1900's up to the 1940's the price of green rice was not very established as it was harvested mainly to be used as a good storable, nutritious food to be used during the long, cold winter months to feed the family. The wild rice that was sold or traded was worth 25 cents or less per pound. Some of the finished wild rice was used by the Indians to trade with merchants for items they needed, but mainly it was the native furs the traders wanted, especially beaver hides. In the 1940's and 50's some merchant-minded men recognized an opportunity to make profits in buying and selling finished wild rice. The restaurants catering to the gourmet tastes of the wealthy were willing to pay good prices to obtain this new "wild" grain from the Northern interior lakes of America and Canada. In the 1950's and 60's traders started to purchase green wild rice and set up their own processing plants. They developed some crude machines to mechanize the roasting/drying, hulling and cleaning of the wild rice.

The traders who purchased the green wild rice, and then processed and marketed the finished wild rice became very competitive in securing the limited supply. They provided free canoes to harvesters, offered higher prices, and had the buyers at lakeside with sacks, a scale, cash and a truck. They started flying the crop before it matured to determine where the best stands of wild rice were located so they could have their buyers at that location. In the late 1950's and early 1960's the buying of green wild rice became so competitive between buyers in Minnesota that it became a "no-bars" struggle to gain control of supply. The price would fluctuate daily and harvesters would seek out the buyer with the highest price. Pickers would go from buyer to buyer and line up to sell their day's harvest, or hold their pick for a couple days waiting for the prices to go up. The limited supply in lean crop years, the high prices for finished wild rice in the expanding markets, and the inability to increase production were reasons for enterprising minds to think about ways in which production could be increased by *domesticating wild rice.*

The first attempts to grow the crop were done by seeding private owned shallow lakes or by diking flatland adjacent to water. Wild rice harvested from a lake was used to seed the lake or "paddy". The owner was now able to control the water levels and eliminate one of the major hazards of poor harvests on the public lakes. There was no governmental control of dates, time or method of harvest on private land. New types of harvest equipment were invented to enable the owner to harvest a crop with minimum cost. Handicaps in this way of producing wild rice were the inability to solve the other factors causing damage to the crop--shattering by storms, plant density, frost, and insects. A leader in this effort to increase production by "growing" the wild rice was James Godward and his brothers who developed paddies on land they owned at Cross Lake, Minnesota.

A contractor in the Twin Cities, Algot Johnson, had a hunting cabin on Squaw Lake, Minnesota, where he took his guests to shoot an abundance of ducks that came in to feed in the large wild rice beds. This attempt being made by others to grow wild rice, along with the efforts being made at the University of Minnesota to develop a non-shattering strain of wild rice, intrigued him to get involved in this new exciting adventure. In the early 1960's he located some flatlands adjacent to the Tamarac River at Waskish that was owned by the State of Minnesota. He negotiated a lease, which would allow him to develop paddies to grow wild rice. He hired a local farmer to develop the land to grow wild rice. Franklin Kosbau, who owned a small track dozer, was skilled at mechanics, was good at operating equipment, and had a lot of ambition,

17

got the job. The paddies were developed and seeded, and now the ideas of Algot would be put into practice to try to domesticate wild rice.

The wild rice, like all other grain, matures in stages starting at the top of the head. Due to shattering the mature kernels fall whenever the plant is disturbed. How to capture the kernels as they drop without destroying the plant was the challenge. Since wild rice grows in lakes it was assumed that the plant required water throughout the entire life of the plant. One idea was to tie the heads together, as was being done by some Native Americans in lakes, so the plant had more stability and not shatter. This required too much time and labor. Another idea was to build containment areas out of plastic that would hold water, cut the wild rice before maturity, shock it and place it in the water containers to mature, like they do with grain. The problem was that when the wild rice was cut off, the nutrients needed to mature the immature kernels were gone and the green kernels dried up, shriveled and were of no value. One more attempt was made by stringing cables across the fields to guide machines made out of grain harvesters on floats to harvest the wild rice as it matured. This would require several passes through the field as the wild rice ripened. This method was very slow, needed a lot of power to pull the machine through a dense stand, and was not acceptable. As a salvage effort, a call went out for people to pick the rice the traditional way with canoe and sticks. There was not a sufficient response as people were more interested in harvesting wild rice on public waters and selling to buyers at the premium prices.

After the second year Algot was out of ideas for growing and harvesting the paddy wild rice. He told Franklin, "You can have the crop if you can harvest it." This was a challenge that excited Franklin. For the next three long days and short nights he bolted 4' timbers on the tracks of his crawler dozer, built a 28' header to mount on the dozer arms, and he launched his invention into the stands of maturing wild rice. It trampled down the wild rice where the tracks went, but the header was wide enough to cover a much wider non-trampled area, representing 71% of the crop. Every other day the machine would travel over the same tracks and harvest the newly matured wild rice. This method proved successful as it could be done by one person, was not too costly, and was dependable.

When Algot decided to give up the crop, he sold his development to an old friend who lived near his hunting cabin, Bud Anderson of Max, Minnesota. Bud was involved in buying lake wild rice and had been observing the nice stands of wild rice grown in man-made paddies. He wanted to employ Franklin to continue the management of the project, but this did not appeal to Franklin's sense of independence. There was a 40-acre parcel of State-owned flatland adjoining Algot's parcel, which could be leased. It would take funds to develop the land for paddies and banks were skeptical of this new adventure.

Franklin's brother Harold was a business education teacher in Aurora, Minnesota, and had been observing this new crop being grown in his hometown of Waskish. Franklin approached him to see if he was interested in becoming a partner in this new adventure. With Franklin's new harvester invention, and a $3,500 investment by Harold, a joint venture was formed, named Kosbau Brothers. The land was leased, diked and planted. The first crop was a nice stand and a good yield. Word had gotten out to the buyers about this new source of wild rice. Harold was helping with the harvest and staying with his parents, Frank and Elizabeth Kosbau. Franklin turned the sales over to Harold as he was busy with the harvest and tired from the work. The buyers were competing to buy all of the wild rice from this first harvest and begin a phone calling campaign to see if they could make the highest and acceptable bid. It was exciting for Harold to be a part of this new race to buy the wild rice. He had never seen such competitiveness. Each call would be an offer at a higher price. It narrowed down to two bidders, Ben Hoffman and Clifton Nelson. As the hour got late, and Harold too needed to rest for the harvest of the next day, the decision was made to sell to Ben.

The following year Clifton would win with his persistence. On a harvest day he called and wanted to talk with us, so Franklin said "OK". Clifton arrived about 9:00 p.m. when we were exhausted and ready for bed. We sat and talked and, as the night wore on, mainly listened. Franklin had a large smoked whitefish of which we had eaten about 1/4th. He offered it to Clifton, who gladly accepted. He ate and talked until the wee hours of the morning and had eaten all of the fish. At 3:00 a.m. Clifton stated, "Well I better let you guys get to bed." We enthusiastically agreed, and we "crashed" for a couple hours before starting another labor-intensive day.

The paddies were drained at harvest time to provide better ground conditions for the track harvester. This took away the water that stabilized the plants. As a result, the roots in the wet, soft soil would not support the plants when a strong wind put pressure on them and the plants would fall over and lodge. The drainage was needed to be able to do tillage and incorporate the large amount of plant material for decomposition. It could not be burned, as the topsoil was peat, which is a combustible organic material. The track dozer and a light disk were used to breakdown the plant material and open up the soil for aeration so it could dry enough to support rubber-tired tractors and heavier equipment.

The stability of the plants and lodging due to wind and heavy rains was a problem and led Franklin to experiment with draining the water before the plants matured. The question was, how dependent is the wild rice plant on standing water during the later stages of growth? When Franklin drained the water two weeks before expected harvest, he found that there was no affect on the plants growth. The soil became firm, the roots grew downward for moisture, and the plant could withstand the forces of a wind. Plus, now with more firm soil the harvester did not sink in as deep, and it was much easier to harvest and work the soil after harvest. This discovery that wild rice does not depend on water in the later stages was one of the basic advancements in the development of wild rice as a farm-grown cultivated crop.

A crawler tractor had worked as the initial harvester, but it had some weaknesses. It was too heavy requiring the 48" planks on the tracks to prevent it from sinking in too deeply in the soft soil. This caused a lot of wild rice to be trampled and lost after the first of several passes in the maturing rice. The first header was a trough-like container with a paddle reel hitting the heads and sending the ripe kernels into the pan. A lot of the kernels fell to the ground before reaching the container. Franklin started to develop the concept of a better harvester. He took his ideas to Ray Motter who owned a small, one-man machine shop in Cohasset, Minnesota. Ray had all of the shop equipment needed, the experience, and the desire to build a model of Franklin's ideas. A narrow-track machine was designed and built which would be as light as possible powered by a small industrial Ford engine and hydrostatic drive. Pointed 3' long aluminum pans were attached to the front of the header to catch the falling kernels that were dislodged by the paddle reel. The model was tested on Kosbau Brothers paddies at Waskish. See Pic. 6. Like anything new some minor changes had to be made, but the Motter Harvester was the best machine to date for harvesting shattering wild rice.

Pic. 6 The First Motter Harvester

There was too much plant material after harvest, and the disc was not doing a satisfactory job. The tough stems would bunch up and plug the disc. Franklin and Harold went to look at an Int'l Tractor, Model 806, with a 100" Howard Rototiller at Hasskamp Implement in Aitkin, Minnesota. Both units were on sale for $6,500. They tried it out and were satisfied with the way it shredded the plant material, aerated the soil, and made a level bed for the following year's crop. See Pic. 7. The First Northwestern Bank of Grand Rapids, Minnesota, (W. King, President, was interested and supportive of a new industry) made a loan to Kosbau Brothers in July 1965 to purchase the first soil preparation equipment to be used in the new paddy wild rice industry. They were also able to work up new land with the tractor and tiller. The tiller would tear up raw moss, grass, brush and small trees. When other new prospective wild rice growers saw what it would do, they wanted Kosbau Brothers to come and work up their new ground.  In one year they had earned enough to pay off the loan, and made a gain on the investment. This method of working the raw land and the wild rice paddies became the best way to work the organic soils and led to the sale of many tractors with dual tires and Howard rotovators made in England to new paddy wild rice growers.

In 1966 Kosbau Brothers decided to expand and purchased 80 acres on the Tamarac River from Mrs. Ellen Carlson.  About 60 acres were ditched and diked, tilled up and put into production.   Now with this new private-owned land and the State leased acres, they had about 80 acres in wild rice.   They purchased a second Motter Harvester to be able to harvest the shattering wild rice before it fell on the ground.

Pic. 7 Franklin on Int'l Tractor and Howard Rototiller

In the mid-1960's the lake production was at a low and

23

supply was short. Demand was high and prices were at an all time high. Besides growth in the traditional markets of high-class restaurants and specialty stores, industrial markets became interested in blending wild rice with other products to add taste and value. A white rice company in Houston, Texas, Uncle Ben's, Inc., had developed and promoted a retail package with a blend of white and wild. To fill the initial orders created by the large promotional advertising, they needed more wild rice than any other one market had ever purchased. In 1966 only a few buyers had the quantities of wild rice that they needed. Clifton Nelson had anticipated a short crop and had purchased most of the crop, including the Kosbau Brothers second paddy crop at $2.75 per lb. green. Uncle Ben's ended up purchasing their supply from Clifton Nelson at $8.00 per lb. When this price information got out to the public, the "gold rush was on." It was said, "In the Clearwater area from the air all of the backhoes working to make wild paddies looked like a flock of wild geese."

With the high prices as an incentive, the harvest of lake grown wild rice was attracting new harvesters by the droves. People from as far away as the Twin Cities were taking their vacations at a time to coincide with the opening of the wild rice season. This was regulated by the Dept. of Natural Resources, who determined the dates, harvest hours, and which lakes were open to harvest. There would be long lines of traffic heading north with canoes strapped on the top of cars and pickups. The competition got so intense that people were harvesting the wild rice before it would mature. The buyers were so competitive that they were buying the immature wild rice. It was being sold and purchased by the weight, so unscrupulous, get-rich-quick, harvesters were adding sand in the bags and were soaking them in the lake to add water. The yields and quality of the finished wild rice was being decreased. The lakes were being over-harvested and the crop was in danger of being severely damaged.

The new industrial user of wild rice decided to put a representative in the area to look out for their interests. In 1967 Uncle Ben's moved Wayne Lamke to Grand Rapids, MN. They had heard about the new efforts to grow wild rice in paddies by the Kosbau Brothers. They made contact with Franklin and Harold about buying all of their production. Selling the entire crop to one buyer at a predetermined price seemed interesting to the Kosbau Brothers, as they had wondered who would buy their crop when a bumper lake crop came along. A contract was written up with Uncle Ben's to buy the entire crop of finished wild rice. This meant that Kosbau Brother would have to locate a processor to dry, hull, clean and bag the wild rice. This started a new phase where the producer owned the wild rice until it was dried/finished and ready for market.

Neighbors and people from a distance away were observing what Kosbau Brothers was doing to grow wild rice on land in low areas adjacent to streams. They had similar land and expressed a desire to grow wild rice. Kosbau Brothers discussed the sale of wild rice from these growers with Uncle Ben's, which had stated a need for more wild rice than we were producing. A contract arrangement was made between Kosbau Brothers and growers wherein Kosbau Brothers would provide wild rice seed and assistance in growing wild rice. The crop grown would be delivered to Kosbau Brothers as it was harvested from the field. A sample of each load was taken and one-half the sample was sent by Greyhound bus to a laboratory in Minneapolis to be analyzed for yield. The remaining one-half was kept in case the shipped sample was lost enroute, and placed in refrigeration for safe keeping until the results were received. The grower was paid based on green weight and a calculated yield based on the results from the Minneapolis lab. It would usually take about one week to get the lab report after the samples were shipped. The growers were anxious to get the lab results sooner as this would help them know if the wild rice was mature enough to continue with the harvest.

In 1967 Harold changed from teaching high school in Aurora to teaching and head of the business department at Itasca Junior College in Grand Rapids. The lab analysis and report system in Minneapolis was not satisfactory, so Harold discussed the idea of setting up a lab for wild rice in the Grand Rapids area with Robert Schwob, a science teacher at Itasca Junior College. He would be ideal as he had experience in calculations and computers, and would be impartial. When this idea was discussed with Wayne Lamke of Uncle Ben's, he talked to his superiors in Houston, Texas, and they volunteered to provide the equipment and training if Schwob was interested in setting up a lab. Schwob talked with Uncle Ben's representatives and went ahead with setting up a lab in the attic above his garage. The lab was named Northern Rice Lab. This proved to be a very beneficial service for a rapidly growing paddy wild rice industry that was producing a green wild rice with a wide range of yields.

The first pickers dislodged the mature kernels with a reel and board bats. This caused some heads and plant leafs to be mixed with the wild rice. To remove this waste material from the wild rice, Kosbau's acquired an old threshing machine which they modified and setup in a new steel building with cement floor they had built on their parents land two miles north of Waskish. They removed the cylinders and ran the rice over the screens and shakers. The airflow from the blower through the screens cleaned the wild rice of foreign materials. Now the clean wild rice was ready to be hauled in a grain truck to a processing plant to be dried, hulled, scarified, cleaned and sized.

In 1967 the green wild rice was hauled to Clifton Nelson's plant at Outing, Minnesota. The plant was set up in an old wooden building. The parchers (dryers) were large drums with paddles stirring the wild rice as it was being heated by gas or wood. We were a bit apprehensive as the wood fires in a wooden building looked like "a disaster waiting to happen." Each parcher would hold several hundred pounds of green wild rice. When the wild rice was dried to a moisture level of about 10% or less, it was dumped and transferred to a hulling machine. After the hulls were loosened from the kernel in a fast rotating drum, the batch was removed and went through aspiration to remove the hulls. Then on to further cleaning and grading in indent and gravity machines. The finished wild rice was bagged in 100 lb. bags and stored on pallets for shipment to a buyer. This whole process was done for 25 cents per pound.

Seed for the new acres being developed had to be cleaned and set aside from the green wild rice. Knowing that the natural lake wild rice fell into the lake for future growth, we assumed that the wild rice could not be allowed to dry out. We placed it in nylon bags and weighed an amount of wild rice that would seed two acres, which was 60-70 lbs. The bags were placed in large cattle watering tanks and filled with water. See Pic. 8. These tanks were covered with plywood and lowered into a ditch or pond for winter storage. The tanks would be removed in the spring and the seed would be broadcast by hand in the paddies. This method had some problems with keeping a supply of fresh water on the seed, with muskrats chewing holes in the bags, and in the handling of the large tanks. There was an artesian well on Kosbau's parent's land, so they decided to build an insulated building with a large cement holding tank next to the well. The flow from the well was diverted to flow through the tank and supply fresh water throughout the winter months. See Pic. 9. This proved to be very good storage for the seed, which now could be stored in bags. In the spring when it was time to spread the seed in the paddies, the seed bags would be taken out and set to allow the excess water to drain off. Even though there was a fresh flow of cold water over the wild rice, it still took on a bad odor, like rotten eggs. It was not a pleasant job to handle the wild rice. As acreage to plant got larger, airplanes were used and the wild rice was mixed 50/50 with dry oats so the grain would flow out of the plane. After several years it was discovered that the seed could be broadcast in the fall with a fertilizer spreader and worked into the soil before the ground was frozen. The moist ground and snow cover protected the seed and maintained the viability of the seed. Spring seeding was continued when a farmer wanted to delay the planting to set back the harvest date.

Pic.8. Daughter Cathe setting on new seed tanks.

Pic. 9. Deloris & Mom K. new seed bldg.

If paddies were going to produce year after year, the nutrients in the soil needed to be replenished. It was assumed that wild rice needed the basic nutrients

28

required by other farm crops, which are nitrogen, phosphorus and potash. There were no established guidelines for fertilizing wild rice like there were for other farm crops, which had been grown for 100's of years. The plants were losing the dark green color during the growing period, especially when the plants were starting to develop heads. This meant the plant was lacking in nitrogen. The best form of nitrogen for top-dressing was urea at 46% because it was slower at converting to nitrates, which could be taken up by the plants. Due to the water and plants 3-4 ft. tall, the only method to apply was airplane. Nelson Aero-Ag from Elbow Lake, Minnesota, was contacted and flew his crop-spraying plane to Waskish to fly on the nitrogen. Within a couple days there was visual response to the nitrogen application. After the fields were rototilled at least twice in the fall, a mixture of the three basic nutrients was broadcast with a spreader. A field drag was pulled over the paddies to incorporate the fertilizer and level out the soil. The nearest plant selling fertilizer was 40 miles away and did not handle the blend of nutrients wanted by Kosbau Brothers for their paddies. Olin was selling urea and a blend of nutrients wanted, so Kosbau Brothers became a dealer for Olin fertilizer. Besides supplying their own needs for fertilizer, they sold fertilizer to the growers who were contracting their crops with Kosbau Brothers. No equipment was available to weigh or handle bulk fertilizer, so all of the fertilizer came in 90 lb. paper, poly-lined bags.

All of the wild rice that dropped on the ground from the shattering plants became seed that would grow the following spring when the paddies were flooded. If there had been some severe storms before or during harvest, there was a surplus of 75% or more of the seed needed to grow the next crop. This meant the crop was so dense there was not enough space, nor nutrients for all of the plants to grow and be healthy. A way to thin the crop needed to be developed. In April-May when the plants grew a floating leaf it could be determined if the stand was too thick. The first thinners developed were crossbars on hay rake wheels. They were hitched together and pulled behind a tractor or track harvester. This method did thin the crop, but it was too slow at 2 acres per hour, and caused the seedbed to be disturbed and uneven. Franklin was thinking of a better way to thin when he was watching a show on television about airboats in Florida. He found a manufacturer in Lake Hamilton, Florida. The idea of using the airboat for thinning wild rice was discussed with the manufacturer. The boat was powered by a 180 h.p. Lycoming engine. This seemed like a lot of power to harness to something that would thin the wild rice. Even though it seemed like it might work, and if it did we might become dealers, the manufacturer was not willing to supply us with a trial model. He would let us try one though if we came to the factory in Florida. Franklin was real busy, so he sent Harold off to explore the possibilities of the airboat.

After a speedy trip to Lake Hamilton, Florida, Harold was at the factory. The plant was next to the lake and had a boat for trying out. It was a small shallow lake with an island in the center. With Jim Combee as the driver, and I as the observer, we headed for the island. In seconds it planed on the water and we were gliding at a speed of 30 M.P.H. at medium throttle. As we came up to the grass and brush laden island, we proceeded to go right up over the land pushing down the grass and brush. It did not seem like there was much that would stop this flat-bottomed, fiberglass airboat. It was about 7 1/2 ft. wide and 11 ft. long. You could spin it in circles as the air blast from the propeller hit the two wide moveable air fins on the back of the boat. I asked about snakes and Jim told me, and later showed it to me, that one of their workers had killed a 6 ft. water moccasin on the island the day before. As we cruised on the lake we would see the backs of alligators swimming. We went into one small harbor-like area where Jim said there was an 18 ft. deep hole wallowed out by a huge female alligator. I sure hoped we would stay afloat as we spun around in the hole. I took the driver seat and hesitantly did a few maneuvers with it, while I kept one eye out for alligators. It seemed to me that this airboat would be the fast, powerful piece of equipment we needed to thin wild rice. After calling Franklin and reviewing my observations with him, I purchased the airboat with the understanding that they would take it back if it did not do the job for us. As I traveled home with my pickup and the airboat on a trailer, I got many inquiries when I stopped as to what it was and where I was going with it, especially as I got in the northern states.

When I got back to the new shop at Aitkin, Franklin went to work on trying to attach something to the back of the airboat that would function as a thinner in the wild rice. He made a bar the width of the boat and inverted dump rake teeth to get the curvature and spring to go over any objects. He got some carbon steel in two-inch strips from a supplier. The steel strips were welded in a V formation, attached to the rake teeth, and sharpened on the side that would be forward. A hand lever was placed near the driver's seat and rods attached to the cutting bar so it could be raised at the end of the field. The raising of the bar was necessary for the boat to turn quickly. This experimental model worked very well. We were now able to thin at 20+ M.P.H., or about 20 acres per hour, and the cutters were close to the bottom where the wild rice plants were cut off close enough to the roots that they would not grow back. The V cut removed over 50% of the excessive growth. See Pic. 10. Now we could thin at least 10 times as fast as we had done previously and there was no damage to the soil. If after thinning once, the plants were still too dense, we could quickly spot thin it a second time. There were getting to be a fairly large number of growers in Northern Minnesota and they were experiencing the same problems of having too dense stands in second and succeeding year crops. They too were trying to design a machine to do a better and faster job of thinning. When they observed the airboat thinning, they were amazed at its performance and were eager to buy an airboat thinner. We got a dealership to sell airboats and built the thinner attachments in our shop. We sold at least 20 of the airboat thinners to other growers in the Minnesota paddy wild rice industry and even sold some to the lake harvesters in Canada. I took Hal and Greg with me to Lac LaRonge, Saskatchewan, when I demonstrated the airboat for Kaz Parada, who was seeding wild rice in shallow lakes, and had this same problem of having too thick stands. This was a high school graduation fishing trip for Hal. Kaz let us stay in his lake cabin and Hal and Greg went fishing while I demonstrated the airboat. I did get in one day of fishing for walleyes.

Pic. 10. Airboat thinning wild rice

Our wild rice paddies at Waskish were doing well, but the terrain in that area was not easy for us to expand our acreage. There seemed to be too much timber, which made it costly to clear and develop. Flat and open areas were private owned and limited. Franklin went exploring in the early 1970's for an area that had large flat areas adjacent to water where we could expand and develop at minimum cost. He located some state land along the Little Willow River in Aitkin County that looked attractive. Access to the land was not easy because there was a private 40-acre tract owned by Jasper Pratt between the state land and the road. Franklin told me about his find and that we should see if Pratt would sell us the parcel. Here was my next assignment. I went to see Pratt and asked him if he was interested in selling the 40-acre piece. He said, "It was too wet for him to cut hay on and he would consider selling it for $5.00 an acre." I was delighted with his offer and accepted. He apologized for setting the price so high because he had bought it for $2.00 an acre. Pratt also sold us a 2-acre lot of high ground in the corner of his field along the township gravel road on which we built our shop. Franklin moved in a trailer house next to the shop so he and his wife, Deloris, could be near the new development.

We hired Duane Brandon in Waskish to manage the paddies while we were developing the paddies in Aitkin County. Franklin had just built a new home at Waskish, so he was back and forth between Waskish and Aitkin. To further complicate matters, we purchased over 800 acres of potential wild rice land on an auction of County land. This was located 1/2 mile north of Jenkins Lakes and south of Palisade. Now we had two large sites about 15 road miles apart in Aitkin County being developed to grow wild rice.

The site at Waskish became too much for us to manage.

Ray Berger had a small store near our paddies on the Tamarac River and he had expressed an interest in our paddies. We negotiated a sale of the paddies to Berger. He also decided to buy Franklin's new home. Our mother had died in 1968, and it got so our father could not live alone in the country. Velmer Halama purchased the land and buildings, which had been our parent's home and the home base of our operation. Our father was over 80 years old and was ready to move to town. We purchased a trailer home for him and set it up on a lot in Kelliher next to foster-son Tony Okerlund's laundry mat.

Our shop on Pratt's land was on a gravel road, which got very soft in the spring and had weight restrictions. We had a semi-truck and trailer, and a Caterpillar backhoe, which needed to be moved to various locations. We needed to have our shop located on a year-around, non-restricted highway. Harold Ramsdell had a 93-acre farm on Hwy. 169 for sale. It was only 3 miles away from the farm, with a house and barn, and was on the Mississippi River. We purchased it and had Glen Oleson build us a metal, insulated shop on the SE corner close to the highway. Franklin and Deloris moved into the house with their two children, Bradley and DeeAnn. We purchased a 10' by 57' trailer home and set it up along the Mississippi River for Harold, Betty, and children (Hal, Cathe, Greg and Tammy), to live in during the spring to fall period.

In 1970 Harold left his teaching position at Itasca Junior College to take a year-around active role in the farm and business. We were starting to get a lot of projects going to supplement the costs of developing our two farms in Aitkin. We had a contract with Uncle Ben's to buy and sell to them our own and other grower's wild rice. We were a dealer for chemicals and fertilizers with Olin, so we were selling these to other growers from spring to fall. We had a dealership for the airboats, and another from

Berkeley Pumps to sell the high-volume, low-lift pumps used in flooding the wild rice paddies. When our backhoe, with long tracks and wide pads, wasn't busy on our farm, it was out doing custom work for others--developing paddies for other growers which needed ditches and dikes, digging stock and wildlife ponds, and cleaning ditches for townships and the county. We also did custom work for other farmers with our tractors plowing and discing new or large acreage.

Franklin had been involved in the selection of non-shattering wild rice plants when he worked for Manomin Development at Deer River. After 2 years he left them to allow him more time to develop his own paddies. He selected lake-grown seed, which he thought had good non-shattering characteristics. Small seed plots were developed at Waskish and later at Aitkin. To assist us in the development of the seed we made an agreement with Green Giant to assist us in the plant breeding. Dr. Karl Kaukis, a sweet corn plant breeder, was designated to be the plant breeder on this project. Our visits to the research plots at Green Giant were interesting, and we were grateful for the generous samples of mushrooms from the growing rooms. We worked together for two years until management in Green Giant decided to discontinue research work on wild rice. This left us alone again, but the seed was ready to multiply and use for production. We had enough seed to plant in small paddies of two varieties. Our names for the varieties were K-1 and K-2, with the K standing for Kosbau.

Research in plant breeding to develop a non-shattering variety of wild rice got started at the University of Minnesota in the early 1960's, but was discontinued due to a lack of funding for new research. Two plant breeders who were involved in this research so believed in the possibilities of developing a new variety that would not shatter they left the University of Minnesota. Enthusiasm to domesticate the FIRST cereal grain in the North American Continent spurred them on to continue in this effort with private employers. Erwin Brooks, who had been working on his doctorate in plant breeding, was employed by Manomin Development to head their research plots located on the Francis Brink farm at Deer River. Algot Johnson hired the other plant breeder to do private research for him. In 1969 the first non-shattering variety was planted in Aitkin County several miles north of Palisade on land owned by Algot Johnson. It was named the Johnson variety. A large crowd of growers came to see this first harvest with an Int'l track combine, which would cut and thresh the wild rice. The wild rice was 7 ft. or more in height, had large heads, wide leaves, and stooled out with over 20 tillers. The plush growth would prove to be a disadvantage because it harbored the moisture on the plants and was very susceptible to lodging and disease.

Growers in the Clearwater area who were just getting started in developing paddies purchased the seed of the Johnson variety and went wild with developing new acres. Stanton and Ray Skoe were developing large acreage north of Clearbrook. Clifton Nelson, Dr. Keith Stolen and Ordeen Sundrud developed 3,500 acres in a few years near Trail, Minnesota. All this development in a short span of time would turn out to be a disaster for the wild rice industry. With a fairly large lake crop in the same time period, and all of this new paddy production, the limited markets were not able to absorb the huge increase in supply. In addition, the processing plants could not process the wild rice fast enough, so there were large quantities of perishable green wild rice piled up three months after harvest that was moldy and had a putrid odor. This late processed wild rice from molded green wild rice caused broken kernels with white ends in processing, had a bad odor, and was not fit to eat. Yet it was forced into the market at low prices by the over-zealous producer/marketers. There was a very negative reaction from the buyers and consumers who were familiar with wild rice as a fresh, nice-smelling, roasted grain, which was a delight to eat. An industry that had a good reputation hurt its image with the public. There got to be huge amounts of broken kernels, which were not acceptable to the markets. To sell the broken kernels the price had to be cut to less than one-half of whole grain prices. The wild rice soup market was built on using the broken kernels at a much lower price. It took several years to overcome the bad image from the bad taste and depressed prices due to overproduction. New processing plants were built to handle the increased production and process the perishable green wild rice within a 10-day period to preserve its quality. New grower cooperatives were organized to develop new markets for the several million pounds of excess wild rice. Before this large increase in production there had only been markets for less than one million pounds in a single year.

Pic. 11. MF Combine, 510, 1/2 track,
Harold Kosbau & Jim Renner

Franklin and Harold planted the seed grown in plots in new paddies at Aitkin. They purchased two Massey Ferguson, Model 510, with half-tracks, see Pic. 11, to harvest the non-shattering wild rice. The two varieties were not truly non-shattering, but they were the best in the industry developed to date. They were 5-6 ft. tall, had medium width leaves, and several tillers on an average. The yield per acre was up to 1,000 lbs. with 42% recovery. After growing the K-1 and K-2 varieties in paddies for two years, in 1972 Kosbau Brothers made the decision to sell seed to other growers on a contract. They were not allowed to sell any of their production to other growers. We did not want growers who had purchased our seed going out to the industry and selling it like they were doing the Johnson seed. This restriction was meant to help prevent over-production that would further depress prices. Also, we wanted to maintain the quality of the seed by not mixing it with lake or Johnson seed. They were to pay a commission on their production to Kosbau Brothers for five years. The K-2 variety proved to be the better of the two, so K-1 was discontinued. See Pic. 12 of grandsons Nathan and Joseph standing near field of K-2 being harvested. Seed was taken only from paddies which were newly developed and had not been used for growing the shattering wild rice. Wild rice seed has been known to stay viable in damp soils below the 3-inch growing layer for several years. We did not intend to continue developing new varieties, so we gave the University of Minnesota permission to use K-2 in their wild rice plant breeding research. The K-2 variety has now been used for 30 years by plant breeders at the University of Minnesota to cross with many other wild rice plants to develop a new variety that will have the desired characteristics. In the early 2000's a variety was released to growers that had been developed by Dr. Raymie Porter, Plant Breeder, University of Minnesota, that has greatly increased yields and shows resistance to fungus diseases.

Pic. 12 Nathan and Joseph by field of K-2 wild rice.

The farm in Morrison township continued to increase in size. As adjoining parcels of land came up for sale, private and public, Kosbau Brothers purchased them. About 50% of it had been farmed in the early 1900's, but was abandoned due to wetness and lack of drainage. Neighbors who had lived in the area for many years told us that this land could never be farmed. The Little Willow River meandered through the flatlands and had beaver dams in it to restrict the flow. A ditch had been dug in the early 1900's between the Little Willow River and the Mississippi, a distance of 3 miles, to help relieve the Little Willow River of excess flows in spring thaw or large rainfalls. This ditch was plugged from one end to the other with brush, erosion of the banks, and beaver dams or plugged culverts. The first job we did was to clean old ditches, open or replace culverts, and dig new ditches to drain the land we intended to develop. This dried up the land and allowed us to drive dozers and tractors on the undeveloped land. We ditched, built dikes and roads, and tilled up the brush, trees and grass. Neighbors were amazed that we could drive rubber-tired tractors where they had only dared go with horses, and at times not even with horses. In fact, if it had not rained, we could drive pickups and trucks in the fields.

Land was purchased on both sides of the "overflow" county ditch in Morrison township until we had acquired over 2,300 acres. The land was in Sections 8, 9, 15, 16, 17, and 21. Most of the land on the west side of the ditch had been farmed, and several hundred acres had been planted to pine and spruce trees under a USDA tree-planting program. It was too wet for the trees on most of the land and the trees did not survive. There was a nice stand of Norway pine trees on about 20 acres of high sandy soil, which we saved. Our children--Hal, Cathe, Bradley and DeeAnn--who were in their early teens, were hired to cut the lower limbs and thin the stand. They were enthusiastic at first, but it got to be a tedious task as the days passed slowly. The bugs, summer heat, sticky sap, and blisters from sawing and chopping took all of the glamour out of this job. There were other fun jobs for them, like picking up sticks in fields we were clearing, pulling waterweeds in paddies and painting water gates, in which Greg and Tammy joined in the work. Cathe and DeeAnn painted Greg with silver tar-base paint one day because he was bugging them and he looked like the "tin-man".

The land east of the ditch had not been farmed. Most of the land was raw peat with an overgrowth of plants, grass and small tamarack and poplar trees. This had been a favorite wild blueberry patch for some of the neighbors. We were not very popular with them when we tilled this area and turned it into a flat black area. Delmer Hegman was hired with his D-6 to clear the larger timber on 300 acres of mineral soil. The first paddies on the north were identified as A-1 and A-2. As we developed paddies to the south, we went to B-1, B-2, C-1, etc. We had Mille Lacs Electric Coop. put in electric poles to a site between the A and B fields so we could have electricity to power a 10" Berkeley vertical low-lift pump. This pumped about 2,500 gallons of water a minute and would pump enough water to flood the A and B paddies. We built a road along the county ditch and an east-west road between every other set of paddies so we could gain entrance to each paddy. Water was directed to paddies by canals from the pumps. The banks on the canals were made high enough so that the water level was higher than the fields. Control of the water to each field was done with tongue-and-grooved boards in water gates. We had fields lettered from A to G on the west side. See Pic. 13 of aerial picture of paddies on the west side of ditch. On the east side our paddies were lettered from H to J. We paid Mille Lacs Electric Coop. to run a power line for 2 miles so we would have electric power to all 6 pumping sites, our large metal equipment storage building, and our 11,000-gallon diesel storage tank.

Pic. 13. Aerial picture south/north, F to A fields

The Little Willow River was the main source of water to flood the paddies. A permit to pump from the Mississippi was obtained to provide water in years of extreme drought. In 1987 it was so dry we set up a diesel-powered Berkeley 16" pump on the Mississippi River. A pipeline of 24" pipe was run from the pump west to a ditch where the water would run by natural fall westward to the county ditch supplying our paddies. This pump's water output at the end of the pipeline was about 5,000 gallons per minute, which was enough to provide some relief from our complete lack of water. When we were fully developed with 1,200 acres in paddies, we had 6 different pumping sites. At each site we could pump enough water to flood 200 or more acres. It would generally take two to three weeks of constant pumping in the spring to initially flood the paddies to a depth of 12 inches. As early in the spring as there was a sufficient flow in the ditch to supply the pumps, the pumps would be thawed out with an electric water heater and flooding of the paddies would start. One year we started in January, and most years it was in March. Some years we had to shovel, or dig with equipment, trenches in snow filled canals so the water could flow to the paddies.

Most of the land on which we grew wild rice was organic (peat) soil ranging in depths from a few inches to 20 feet. The organic soil was ideal for growing wild rice because it held moisture to sustain the wild rice plants needs even when the water was removed 4 weeks before harvest. The peat soil did not get hard like clay soils, which allowed the plant roots to go down for moisture. If it was dry and it rained, the peat would absorb and hold the water. If it was wet at harvest time, the soil would not adhere to the equipment. However, a disadvantage of the peat soil was if it rained too much just before harvest time, the peat would get very soft and would not support the harvest equipment. After struggling through a couple year's of real wet harvests in which the one-half track Massey Ferguson combines were getting stuck or not able to harvest some real wet areas where there was nice wild rice, we went to Davis, California, and purchased two International, Model 915, metal full-track combines. One was for the farm at Aitkin, and one for the farm at Gully.

Pic. 14. Franklin on Int'l
915 all-track combine

Pic. 15. Hal by JD tractor and
14 ft. Northwest rotovator

We bolted 40 inch long oak planks that were 4 by 5 inch to the metal tracks for extra floatation. See Pic. 14 of Franklin on Int'l 915 all-track. In a wet year, these full-track combines could harvest wild rice in the fields with the "soupiest" ground, or where there were holes the half-tracks had been stuck in during previous years. Some years it rained so much prior to or during harvest and the fields were mushy as though they had not been drained. One fall just before harvest we had 11 inches of rain and the fields were completely flooded with several inches of water.

The tractors were 4-wheel drive with dual or triple rice-and-cane tires. We had two John Deere articulating tractors, Models 8640 and 8630, and an Int'l Model 3788,

43

2 + 2. For working up the paddies after harvest we had light tandem discs with large tires. The discs were good to open up the wet soils to hasten the drying and allow more intensive tillage later. If it was too wet to pull a disc, a rototiller was used to cultivate the paddies. Large wheels were put on the rototiller to carry the weight, and power to turn the tiller was done with the power-take-off on the tractor. See Pic. 15 of Hal by a John Deere tractor and tiller. The pole-barn equipment storage building and 11,000 gal. diesel storage tank are in the background.

Combining with a spike tooth MF or Int'l combine was a slow task in a heavy stand of wild rice. The straw had to be dry to not plug up the header or the cylinder. Most mornings it would be close to noon before the dew had dried off the plants enough to start harvesting. During that time the combines would be fueled, greased, cleaned, repaired and checked. Harvest would continue until the dew or fog would set in the evening, which would usually be about 8:00 p.m. An evening hot meal-on-wheels would be provided by Deloris, Betty or Judi so the men could continue harvesting until wetness set in. We could only harvest about 20 acres of wild rice per day with one combine, so when we had 1,000 acres to harvest, we had six combines—2 Int'l 915 full-tracks, 2 Int'l 915 ¾ tracks, and 2 Massey Ferguson half-track combines. See Pic. 16 of Harold with helpers Joseph and Nathan on MF, Model 860, one-half track. One of the MF, Model 750, combines would be used to harvest grain when it was not needed to harvest wild rice. In addition, we had a MF, Model 760 combine, with rasp-bar cylinder, and on rubber tires, to use just in harvesting grain, usually 800 to 1,000 acres.

The grains were barley, fall rye, oats and spring wheat, which would usually mature before the wild rice. In years when ideal weather conditions caused the wild rice to mature early, we would be "stretched" for manpower and equipment to harvest grain and wild rice at the same time.

Pic. 16 Harold, Joseph & Nathan on MF, 860

Various grains were planted on the acres that were not diked for wild rice, and as a rotation crop in the wild rice paddies. The crops grown were barley, rye, oats, wheat, buckwheat, sunflowers, and potatoes. We became certified to grow seed grains by the Minnesota Certified Seed Association so that we could supply the seed to Deerwood Rice & Grain, Inc., which was certified to clean and tag seed grains of specific varieties. These grains then could be sold to other grain dealers or to farmers.

As the Morrison Township farm got larger it became difficult to supply management and equipment for both Aitkin farms. It was decided to sell the Fleming Township (Jenkins Lake) farm. Marshall Diebold, a retired executive of Northrup King Seed Company, and his sons purchased that farm and ran it under the corp. name, DCO, Inc.

Olin stopped manufacturing fertilizer and chemicals. It was hard to find a good supplier in the Aitkin area. Three farms--Kosbau Brothers, Joe Shetka, and Thomas Godward--joined together to form a farm supply company, Pro Farm Supply, Inc. A 26-acre tract of land along Hwy. 210, close to Hwy. 169, on Hassman Corner, was purchased. A storage and office building was designed and built to handle feed, chemicals and fertilizer. Storage tanks and a blender were installed to handle liquid fertilizers. An Ag-Chem truck, 4-wheel drive, floatation tires, with dry or liquid tanks was purchased to custom apply fertilizer. A Ford, 4-wheel drive, 1 ton pickup, with large tires, and a liquid tank and boom was purchased to apply chemicals. The plan was to be able to supply our own farms with quality service, and to offer the supplies and application service to other farmers in the area. The objective was to be able to supply a needed quality service to ourselves and others, and to be able to make enough money to justify our investment. This was started when the farm economy was growing and the future looked good in farming. In the next five years the farm economy declined rapidly and farmers were forced by financial institutions to cease and close down their farms. Our sales dropped off, customers were not able to pay bills and went into bankruptcy, and efforts to take on new projects did not help. To make matters worse, a competitor started business in Aitkin and cut prices to gain our customers. We could not continue to supplement the business with our farms, and made the decision to close the doors on Pro Farm Supply, Inc.

Earl Swenson and Arvid Anderson had a large farm north of Gonvick, Minnesota, and were one of the early farmers with whom we contracted to grow wild rice for Uncle Ben's. They were probably the first to start growing wild rice in the Clearwater River area. After several years of growing they had expanded their wild rice growing to several hundred acres, had over one thousand acres in grain and hay, and had 125 angus and mixed-breed cattle. They decided to sell their farm, and our interest was aroused after observing the production potential of the farm while counseling them about growing wild rice. We had become acquainted with the farming potentials of the land and got to know the values of their farm manager. We talked to some friends about the farm and they were interested in joining us in buying the farm. Gerald Sullivan, a licensed surveyor, and I went out and analyzed the farm for the potential of growing crops and livestock. Based on this survey we made them an offer. In the meantime, about 25 employees of Artic Cat at Thief River Falls were making an offer on the farm, which was higher than our offer. This group ended up owning the farm.

Another farm in this same area, but several miles farther west, was for sale and was called to my attention. I contacted one of the owners who lived in Gully and who owned a farm seed cleaning and sales store. He showed me the farm, which was 10 miles north of Gully. Gerry and I surveyed this farm, which was larger than the other farm, and in our judgment had even greater value for raising crops and livestock. The price was valued right and so we got our future partners together and decided to make the purchase. The partners were Francis Brink, farmer and equipment dealer; Gerald Sullivan, County Surveyor; Harry Chalupsky, lawyer; Franklin Kosbau, farmer, inventor, builder, scientist; Harold Kosbau, business and enterpriser; and Duane Erickson, farm manager of Swenson & Anderson Farm, whom we had gotten to know and thought was the best part of that farm. Duane's attributes were as an all-around handy man, very ambitious, knowledgeable in growing grain and wild rice, and an excellent cattleman who followed all the right techniques in breeding up a high-quality beef herd. The new owners of Swenson & Anderson farm did not want cattle, so we purchased the entire herd and put them under Duane's management. We added neighboring farms that came up for sale until we had 3,300 acres in this farm. We did well until our largest individual owner, Francis Brink, died in an auto accident. We had insufficient life insurance on each other and the need to pay off the widow and children became a large burden. Wild rice prices were declining and we were forced to hold it in inventory, which meant we had to pay the costs of growing out of small grain, hay, and our annual calf sales. The income was insufficient to pay all the costs and to be able to meet our obligation to the Brink family. Two of our partners had sold their interests to Franklin and Harold, so now it was only three left as owners. Then in 1990 Franklin was killed in an accident on a backhoe that went through the ice on a custom job at Palisade, Minnesota. This left Harold and Duane as owners. The work and financial burden became too much, so the decision was reached to sell. Two of the Brink sons, Richard and William, wanted to purchase the Gully farm, so an agreement was reached to sell the farm to them.

The decline in prices on wild rice from overproduction was causing havoc in the whole industry. Our farmer marketing cooperative was losing sales to new producers in California who had discovered they could grow wild rice on white rice farms in the San Joaquin Valley. The price of white rice was depressed and the farmers were looking for a substitute. Due to milder temperatures allowing earlier planting and faster growth, the California crop was two months earlier in maturing and harvest than the Minnesota crop. Our over-zealous buyers were out there encouraging them to grow wild rice, so they could be first in the market place with new crop. This problem would only get worse as the aggressive California farmers and marketers became acquainted with this new crop in agriculture. Like they have done in all of the other new crops they have gotten into growing, they "jumped in with both feet" and a "take-over, get-out-of- our-way" attitude accelerated the growing of wild rice. The Minnesota marketers who had contracted with the California farmers to purchase their wild rice production could not raise the money to buy the wild rice and defaulted on the contracts. The farmers were forced by their bankers to sell the crop at any price. We lost many of our markets to them, as they were willing to sell below their costs to gain market. In a period of several years California exceeded Minnesota as the major production State in the growing of cultivated wild rice.

We had ceased contracting with Uncle Ben's, Inc. in the 1980's due to their buying wild rice from other producers at lower prices and leaving us to hold inventories for them. This tied up our borrowing power with the banks and made it difficult to fund and expand our own farm. We were not sure that this large company would continue buying and marketing wild rice in the long term. They were owned by Mars Candy Company of England and were controlled in their decisions by this large company. The largest cooperative marketing company of wild rice growers invited us to join them. We decided to join and they elected Harold Kosbau as chairman of the Board of Directors. The marketing company owned by the cooperative was named United Wild Rice, Inc.

After several years United Wild Rice, Inc. had built a large modern warehouse/office building in Grand Rapids, had a skilled manager and sales organization, and had increased the annual sales to over two million pounds of wild rice. Some of our members wanted to retire from farming and most of the members wanted to concentrate their efforts on farming instead of marketing. United Wild Rice, Inc.

was large enough so that it was appealing to some very large companies. The company that bought us was not known as a food company, but we found out that one of their main ingredients in making beer is white rice and they were planning to enter into food marketing to sell the excess grain. The buyer was Anheiser-Busch, owned by August Busch III, of St. Louis, MO. In our contract we were bound to sell all of our production of wild rice to them for 3 years. The mistake we made was that they were not obligated to buy all of our wild rice, and we could not sell the extra production to any other buyer. They were playing a new ball game in marketing wild rice, and the California growers now had the advantage. The markets that we had developed were taken over by California, and United Wild Rice, Inc., now owned by Anheiser-Busch, would not take nor pay us for our wild rice. After two years we had 4 million pounds in the warehouse, were bulging at the seams, and had no money for the operating costs of our farms.

Several of us broke our contracts with Anheiser-Busch and formed a new farmer marketing cooperative. We bought out a wild rice marketing company at McGregor, Minnesota, named American Wild Rice. This got us back into marketing our production, but we were not going to break our contract with the largest beer maker and get away with it. A lawsuit was filed against us and we ended up before a judge, who decided that we had to pay $25,000. and forfeit some wild rice as a settlement.

We changed the name of American Wild Rice to Frontier Foods, Inc. and relocated to Aitkin, MN. Two of our members, Robert McGregor and Arnie Lueck, came up with a new method of instantizing wild rice by subjecting the kernels to intense, penetrating heat with ultra-violet. In 15 seconds the kernel would open and expose the inner starches. By adding either hot or cold liquids the wild rice was ready to eat as a breakfast cereal or use as an ingredient. We were all fired up and thought we would have a new breakfast cereal that the public would accept and want to purchase in volumes. We had not taken into account that the shelves are full of cereal and big cereal companies are bombarding the consumer with advertisements to buy a new cereal product. These companies are spending millions on selling their product, and we did not have the money to go out and introduce the public to our product. Besides, everyone was not turned on to wild rice like we were. The wild rice was blended with other ingredients to make a quick heated dish for a side or main dish. Attractive boxes were designed to catch the eye of the consumer as they saw it on the grocery shelf. The food was appealing in taste and nutritional values, but it had to compete with all of the low priced items on the shelf, like the pastas. We could not afford the advertising needed to catch the attention of the consumers, nor did we have the distribution channels to get into the major markets. Through the promotion of the nutritional values of wild rice we were able to enter the diet food markets and made the sale of one of our products to Jenny Craig. Now we were in the big league. That lasted until our quality control missed some pieces of glass in a wild rice shipment to Jenny Craig. We got the semi-load of wild rice back and lost the market. We had put a lot of development costs into the instantizing process and the packaging of it, and were now setting on a large inventory of instant wild rice, fancy boxes, and a financial burden. The group of farmers could not continue subsiding a marketing company, so the vote was taken and passed to sell the marketing company and dissolve our cooperative.

As a sideline in the late 1980's, we had started a garden farm and greenhouse on the 90-acre farm on Highway 169, 10 miles north of Aitkin. Our farm had 1/2 mile of frontage on the Mississippi River from which we could pump the irrigation water for the gardens. Being adjacent to the Mighty Mississippi River, I named our gardening and nursery operation Great River Gardens. We had planted 5 acres of domesticated blueberries, 5 acres of asparagus, and had 20 plus acres of various vegetables, strawberries, raspberries, cole crops and sweet corn. We grew our own transplants in the greenhouse. To generate income in the spring we expanded the greenhouses to growing bedding plants and flowers to sell to the public. Small satellite greenhouses to sell the plants were set up at Deerwood, Aitkin and McGregor. The asparagus and berries were offered to the public on a U-pick harvest. Other produce was harvested and sold at stands or to stores. In the mid 90's the land and business was sold to Joe and Kirsten Riehle, who had been the managers of the operations from the beginning.

Our son, Hal, had assumed the responsibilities of crop management of the Aitkin farm in 1985. He was applying the knowledge in agriculture he had gained at the University of Minnesota, St. Paul, and North Dakota University, Fargo, in the selection of seed, fertilization, weed control and to combat plant diseases. He was promised a share of any gains that he could make on our average production record of crops. In 1985 his excellent record keeping showed a small gain in production, but in 1986 the yields were increased by almost 50%, and Hal earned a bonus equal to 75% of his salary. That fall he was diagnosed with Non-Hodgkins Lymphoma cancer at Mayo Clinic, Rochester. Hal fought a courageous fight but succumbed to this dreaded illness in April 1987. Hal had planned his own funeral, called his Farm House Fraternity friends to be his pallbearers, and asked his Catholic Priest friend to do his service. The Catholic Church in Aitkin, where Hal had been a cantor, was filled with people. Our plans to have Hal succeed us had to be changed. Three months later Franklin and Deloris received the dreadful news that their only son, Bradley, had been killed by someone in Hawaii. The person who killed him has never been found.

Franklin had problems with blockage of the arteries and received three heart bypasses in 1979. Ten years later in November 1989 the same arteries were blocked and he had to have the bypasses done again. He was restricted from doing many kinds of work until the operation was completely healed, a period of at least 3 months for some and more for other more strenuous activities. The last week of February 1990, he had agreed to do custom work with our Komatsu Excavator to clean gravel from a ditch dumping into a lake at Savanna Golf Course, Palisade, and load it on to trucks. Don Frink was our excavator operator, but Franklin decided to help him by moving the machine from our shop to the site of the digging. He unloaded the excavator off the lowboy at the golf course a half-mile from the digging site, and decided to travel the machine to the site on the ice in the ditch. They had checked the ice the day before and found it to be over 24 inches thick and strong enough to support the excavator. Part way to the site there was a spot where snow had drifted over the ice and there was only a thin layer of ice. When the machine reached this spot, one side of the machine sank rapidly and the sudden drop of one side caused Franklin to be thrown violently against the metal frame of the cab and lose consciousness. When the machine was found a half hour later or more by the trucker, Mike Johnson, he jumped on to the cab and was waist deep in freezing water. He broke the cab side window and pulled Franklin from the cab up on to the embankment and tried to revive him, but it was too late. The blow had caused internal bleeding from the operation in November, plus there was water in his lungs. Franklin had made many friends in his lifetime and his funeral in

Aitkin filled the church.

After the loss of Franklin as a partner, I had to assume the management of our farm, processing plant, Gully Farm, and maintain the business operations of marketing, finances and tax reporting. It was not possible to sell, discontinue or shut down operations in a short time. The last enterprise to be liquidated was the farm at Aitkin. Lease arrangements were made with a neighboring wild rice farmer, Thomas Godward, to operate the wild rice paddies on a sharecrop basis. The grain farmland was converted to the growing of hay and leased to local farmers who needed hay for their cattle. An auction of the equipment was held in the spring of 1997. The land was put up for sale. A sale agreement on the land was made to sell one-half of the wild rice paddies to Thomas Godward and the other half to Greg Kennedy, who was going to convert them into growing cranberries. The high prices for cranberries had caused an over production and the prices over a couple years dropped to below growing costs. Kennedy could not continue his effort and split his part of the farm between hunting land and the wild rice acres to Thomas Godward.

Thomas Godward was educated at the University of Minnesota agricultural campus, St. Paul, and is a very progressive farmer seeking to increase the crop yields. He is growing wild rice on four farms and has up to 2,000 acres in wild rice production. He has employed Greg Kosbau, our son, as the head mechanic in his shop. Greg graduated in 2003 from St. Cloud University with a teaching degree in Industrial Technology. In 2002 and 2003 Godward hired Nathan Kosbau, Hal's son, to work on his farm. Nathan has a very inquisitive mind and a love for agriculture, so he has developed wild rice seed plots, encouraged and worked on the growing of grains to improve soil nutrients and provide additional income for the farm.  In September 2004, Nathan started classes at Itasca Junior College with intentions of going on to the University of Minnesota, majoring in an agricultural field, like his father.  He applied for a part-time position at the University of Minnesota, North Central Research Station, Grand Rapids, with Dr. Raymie Porter, Wild Rice Plant Breeder.  He was accepted and is working 2 or 3 afternoons each week in the greenhouse, threshing seed, or wherever needed.

Due to constant requests for recipes, Harold and Betty Kosbau had The Herald Review, with Gene Lysaker's artwork, print "Recipes with Wild Rice", December 1970, 55 recipes. By 1974 a second edition had to be printed with over 100 recipes divided into breads, breakfast dishes, combination dishes, deserts, stuffings, salads and miscellaneous. The recipes were the type of dishes used by a housewife to feed her family and the ingredients were the type found in most cupboards or pantries. Most of the recipes were new creations in Betty's kitchen as she experimented with new ways to incorporate wild rice into dishes we enjoyed. Wild rice with its nutty, roasted flavor seemed to harmonize and enhance the flavor of grains, fruits, meats and seafood. Hal, as a teenager, awakened one morning and said to his mother, "I have an idea, mom, about using wild rice with apples in making a cake-like dessert." His mother picked up on the idea and it turned out to be a delightful dessert. It was too late to be entered in the recipe book, but has been used by mom and passed on to her friends many times. The 28,000 life-time supply of recipe booklets have been sold out and no new issues are planned due to the many other fine recipe books that have been published and the increase in costs in producing a 3rd edition.

# An Evolution in Processing

In the 1960's and early 1970's there was a rapid expansion of production. The green combined wild rice from the paddies had higher moisture content than the lake wild rice. This made it more perishable and shortened the time that it could be held after harvest until it was dried or processed. The plants being built or expanded were being done by marketers to handle the green wild rice they were purchasing. Some of them would process wild rice for farmers if they had excess capacity or if they wanted to become middleman between producers and markets. There was very little sharing of information between processors. The processing of wild rice was considered an "art". They had mechanized the way that Native Americans had been processing wild rice and were not willing to share any ideas or techniques with their competitors. Most of them had enclosed buildings for processing and would not allow anyone other than employees to enter the facility.

When we started contracting with Uncle Ben's to sell them finished wild rice, we had to arrange with a processor to agree to take our green wild rice and process it to Uncle Ben's specifications, which were that it must double it's weight in 25 minutes when cooked, and less than 15 percent broken kernels. At first it was not combined and could be held for up to a month if it was not piled too deep, and was aerated and moistened. We drafted up an agreement with a new processor at Ball Club to process all of our wild rice. His plant was not completed, but he assured us that it would be complete by the time we started harvest. When we started delivering the wild rice, he still had some work to do on the plant. Our wild rice sat on the ground unattended for over a month and was spoiling. He finally got the plant started, but was not able to process all of the spoiling wild rice. About one-half had to be hauled to Clifton Nelson's plant at Outing to be processed. It was badly spoiled causing us to lose $50,000 in spoilage and excess breakage. He sued us for the processing fees and we countersued for the losses. The judge ended up not awarding us anything for our losses, but we did not have to pay the processing fees. This experience convinced us that we needed to have a processing plant to protect our perishable green wild rice. After having gone through a whole growing season with all the perils of storms, disease and insects, we did not want to lose the value of the wild rice at the processing plant.

In 1972 Clifton Nelson came to Kosbau Brothers with a proposal to join with him in a 3-way partnership--Clifton, Franklin and Harold--to negotiate a purchase of the defunct loans on the Deerwood Cooperative processing plant. A group of about 100 lake wild rice harvesters had each put in $100. as security for loans from the FHA, EDA and SBA. The balance due on the loans for the steel building, equipment and 3 acres of land was $45,000. We were able to make a contract to buy the entire operation for the balance of the loan. It was a small operation and was not functional the way it was set up. We hired Walt Leas to manage the plant and make the changes needed to make the plant operational. Walt Leas had experience in wild rice processing. He was semi-retired, but was willing to face the challenge of making the plant run again. He was looking for a younger man to assist him and to run the plant when he wanted to go back to retirement. Franklin's brother-in-law, Dan Mohs, had been working in the Twin Cities and wanted to get back up north. He was born and raised on a farm, and his father, George Mohs, had been one of the first growers of wild rice for us with an Uncle Ben's contract. Dan Mohs had worked with equipment on the farm and was a good, all-around handy man. Dan accepted the position of assistant plant manager. In the third year Franklin and Harold decided to buy out Clifton's interest in the plant. They liked the ambition and ability of Dan Mohs and made him the manager of the plant. The plant was reorganized as a corporation and named Deerwood Rice & Grain Processing, Inc. The plant did not have enough capacity to keep Dan busy for much more than 2-3 months in the fall. For the remaining months Dan worked on Kosbau Brothers farm north of Aitkin.

The "Grain" in the name was done with the intention of including small grains in the operation of the plant to buildup another service and sale function to lengthen the seasonal processing into a full year operation. Kosbau Brothers had been growing certified grain seed and had been hauling the grain over 200 miles to the nearest certified seed cleaning plant. A truck scale was installed and certified to weigh incoming grain and wild rice. Two tanks for holding grain and a leg to elevate the grain into the tanks were installed. A large used fanning mill, a gravity table, and an indent machine were purchased. An inspection was requested of the Minnesota Certified Seed Association. They approved the system and granted us a license to clean and tag certified seed. We advertised our service to the regional farmers. We became a dealer for any kind of seed the farmers in our area wanted and accessed it from several wholesalers throughout Minnesota. After a couple years in the grain seed business we became known to other small seed dealers. We purchased truckloads of grain, cleaned and bagged the seed, and sold it wholesale to the small seed dealers in Northern Minnesota and Wisconsin.

Another project taken on by the plant was the sale of feed to the small farms, hobby farmers, and to those feeding birds, ducks and deer. We became a dealer for Heinz Feeds, St. Cloud, Minnesota, who had a reputation for high-quality feeds. The sunflowers for birds was picked up by truck from a supplier at Bagley, Minnesota. This was a nice addition to the wild rice and grain to help fill out the months of the year with activities.

As each of the functions increased and the plant became profitable, all of the profits were reinvested in improving the whole operation. Adjoining land and a house was purchased from Ken Morgan, who had started the original cooperative plant. The land around the plant increased in size from 3 acres to 12 acres. The large trees on a hill behind the plant were cleared off and the hill was leveled and shoved into a low area. The areas along side and behind the plant were blacktopped and dusted with cement to make a storage area for up to one million pounds of green wild rice. The building was expanded to provide more room for wild rice and grain cleaning equipment, more warehouse space to store the finished wild rice and grain, a new office space, and an employee lunchroom and bathrooms.

Green wild rice had to be held by the plant until it could be processed. When harvesters decided to pick lake rice or when farmers decided to pick or combine the wild rice, it was hauled directly into the processing plant, weighed and dumped on the tarmac. At the peak of harvest the plant would receive in one day as much wild rice as it could process in several days. The wild rice was spread out in rows, identified by harvester name, and "cured" until the plant could process the wild rice. "Cured" meant that the wild rice was turned daily and sprinkled with water to release the heat and cool the pile. The heat came from the piling of high moisture green wild rice. The heating had a benefit in causing immature grain to mature. It had a danger in that if the heating was not reduced daily; molds would start to develop on the kernels. This mold would continue to work into the starches of the kernel and eventually destroy the kernel completely. Hot weather with drying winds was also a problem in that it caused the kernels to lose moisture and this would affect the "roasting" to cause more kernels to shatter or break. Extra waterings were required to keep the green wild rice moist.

When we entered the wild rice processing industry in 1972, all of the care of the wild rice being cured was done by hired help using forks to lift and turn the wild rice, and then sprinkle the pile with water from a hose. This was hard, hand-blistering work and it was hard to find people who were willing to do this kind of work day after day. After observing this process for a couple years, Franklin and Harold decided to try and mechanize this "lifting and wetting" of the green wild rice. Franklin talked about a high machine used in spraying corn he had seen in a farm magazine that was manufactured in Iowa by Hagie. We called them to ask where the nearest dealer was located that might have a used machine for sale. They told us there was a machine at Litchfield, Minnesota. This time we both traveled to Litchfield to examine the machine. It had a spacing between the wheels of about 8 ft. with a ground clearance of 5 ft. The drive was hydrostatic, so the ground speed could be varied from a creep to several m.p.h. There were two 300 gal. tanks for carrying water. The machine was exactly what we needed to make it adaptable to turn and water wild rice. Franklin and Dan went to work on constructing a belt conveyor with canvas, sweep paddles to pick up the wild rice, and a hydraulic motor to drive the belt at variable speeds. They suspended it under the machine at an angle with the front sweeping the tarmac surface and the back 3 ft. off the surface. It worked very well and replaced about 50 people at doing a laborious task. After using it for a year, we decided that the plant needed one more machine to handle the larger quantity of wild rice coming to our plant.

Other plants heard about our machine and purchased a machine from us, while others were building their own machines to turn the wild rice. A new and better turning device was made with canvas-tipped paddles to stir the wild rice without lifting it and a spray bar to add water as the wild rice was being stirred. See Pic. 17 and Pic. 18.

Pic. 17 Hagie Wild Rice Turner

Pic. 18 Harold checking wild rice

The University of Minnesota Agricultural Engineering scientists helped to develop equipment for improving the processing of wild rice. A large-volume cleaning machine was designed to take the non-rice materials out of the combined wild rice, such as: plant materials, empty hulls, foreign objects, etc., which amounted to 10 per cent of the weight and 15 percent of the volume. This resulted in a savings in our costs and increased our daily output. They developed a continuous-flow parcher, which worked well, but became too expensive to repair and maintain in operation. The breakage of kernels was a problem in the industry, and they helped identify the causes of kernel breakage.

Deerwood Rice and Grain Processing, Inc.

# Organization
## of New
# Wild Rice Industry

Growers felt a need to work together on their problems. In 1969 they formed an organization named Minnesota Wild Rice Growers Association. Directors elected were Erwin Brooks, Harold Kosbau, Francis Brink, George Mohs and Hilmer Leonhardt. The goals of the organization were--1) to promote wild rice and make consumers of the 75% in the United States who had never tasted wild rice. 2) Talk to State Legislators and the Governor to have research funded at the University of Minnesota. 3) Have an annual meeting to discuss concerns of the members. The organization only had dues for income and a small budget, so little was accomplished other than what volunteer work was done by directors and members. To remedy the lack of funding, a referendum was voted on and passed by the growers in 1974 to form a producer organization with powers to assess growers. It would be regulated by the Minnesota Department of Agriculture. The name chosen was The Minnesota Wild Rice Promotion Council. Growers were elected to the Board of Directors. It was located in Aitkin and the first manager hired was George Moriarty. The Directors voted to assess the growers at 2 cents per finished pound and that the assessment would be collected at the processing plant. The voluntary grower organization changed its name to the International Wild Rice Association and opened the membership to growers, processors and marketers from any state and Canada. George Moriarty was chosen to head both organizations.

George Moriarty had a personality that would win the hearts of everyone. He was a gifted Master of Ceremonies. His jokes and tales would "bring down" the crowd with laughter. After introducing Senator Hubert Humphrey as the speaker at an annual meeting in Grand Rapids, Humphrey stated "I have never been so glad to have an introduction end as this one by George Moriarty." Harold served on the Board of Directors from the beginning, and was president of the Council from 1983 to 1990. He made many trips with Moriarty to the State Legislature to lobby for our industry. On the way home from a long day of lobbying in January at the State Legislature, Moriarty, Former State Senator Dave Rued, and Harold, in Harold's Mercury Marquis, were about 15 miles out of Aitkin near Glen at 9:00 p.m. when a large deer jumped out of the brush alongside the narrow country road right into the windshield. The sound of glass shattering into little pieces was like a gunshot, and glass was spread throughout the car and on its occupants. The hipbone had made a hole in the window, and the deer was ruptured like a balloon, so we were also splattered with blood and gunk. Luckily it was unusually warm for January in Minnesota and I was able to open the side window and stick my head out to see so we could drive 15 miles into Aitkin. Cell phones had not been invented, so we could not call for assistance.

As a new and developing agricultural industry, we had many issues facing us. We needed help from our Local, State and Federal elected officials in many ways. Our issues were as follows: 1) We needed recognition as a new farm crop so we could participate in the many farm programs administered through the State and Federal Dept. of Agriculture. 2) We were in great need of research funding to solve our many problems in growing, processing and marketing. a) How to control diseases and insects that were destroying the crop, and FDA approval of safe chemicals to use. b) What nutrients to add to grow healthy crops and increase yields. c) Develop new varieties that were less shattering, disease resistant, and more productive. d) Improvements in processing the green wild rice to reduce breakage, safely handle a perishable product, speed up the process, and improve quality control. e) Do a nutritional analysis to determine the percentages and values of nutrients in wild rice, and the benefits of eating wild rice by the consumer. f) Develop new recipes and uses for wild rice, and recognition by the food industry and potential consumers. The promotion of wild rice is an on-going process and major objective of the Minnesota Paddy Wild Rice Research and Promotion Council (new name), funded by the Minnesota growers.

We went to Washington, D.C., in 1973 to appeal for Federal funding for wild rice research. Rep. Blatnik, Chairman of the powerful Transportation Committee, with the help of his assistant James Oberstar, was author for our first Federal "Bill" to finance our research at the USDA Laboratory in the House of Representatives. George and I wrote up a formal "Brief" stating the needs of our request for Federal funding, which was typed up in sufficient numbers so each member of the Committee had a copy. The Ag-Sub. Committee to hear our request was headed by the Chairman of the powerful Agriculture Committee-- he was from the State of Mississippi and his interests and knowledge were about white rice. We had been sitting for several hours waiting our turn, and time kept dragging out as speakers took extra time in their presentations. Members of the committee, numbering about 14, kept leaving as it got into the evening hours. Finally at 11:00 p.m. it was our turn to make the last presentation of the day--there were only two members and the Chairman remaining. As the farmer and wild rice grower, I gave the oral introduction of our "Brief". I was nervous and tired as I stood up to make a few comments and read the brief. The Chairman stopped me and said, "There is no need to read the "Brief" as we all have a copy. Just tell us briefly what your needs are and this will all be recorded in the Registry for the members to read." My brain went in a spin, as now I had to rearrange my thoughts and talk with no notes. I was able to draw from my experiences and knowledge enough to convey a meaningful message.

Our next mission was to meet with Senators Hubert Humphrey and Fritz Mondale to develop a parallel "Bill" for funding in the U. S. Senate. Both Senators invited us into their offices and listened intently while we explained what our needs were in our new agricultural industry and what we were requesting in the House of Representatives. They willingly authored a "companion" bill in the U. S. Senate.

The House and Senate Agriculture Committees ended up approving our request, which provided $75,000. of "special" funding for research in processing at the USDA Laboratory, Peoria, Illinois. This "special" meant that the funding would not be renewed in the next Legislative session, and that we would have to come back in two years and make an appeal for continued funding. This was done and after two more appeals for higher and continued funding, the amount was increased to $150,000. and added as a continuing line in the USDA budget. However, the Minnesota Wild Rice Council sent representatives to Washington every two years to insure that wild rice did not get deleted from the budget, as there is always pressure from various agriculture groups to have new funding for their special needs. The funding was changed in the 1990's to provide research funding for an ongoing Wild Rice Plant Breeding project at the University of Minnesota, North Central Research Station, Grand Rapids, Minnesota.

Arrangements were made by Rep. Blatnik's office for us to meet with top USDA officials to tell them about the "newest" domesticated wild cereal grain crop, and explain the urgent needs of the wild rice industry for research at the Peoria Agricultural Research Lab. We were warmly received and appreciated the opportunity to tell our USDA about a new cereal crop being domesticated in Minnesota, and how it was valuable to our economy.

The Wild Rice Council sent George, Nancy and/or myself to food shows for the restaurant and grocery store managers in Minneapolis, Minnesota State Fair, Chicago, Portland, Atlanta, Houston, etc., to introduce and promote the institutional use of wild rice. George and his secretary, Nancy Tetrick, went on the first International trip to promote the use of wild rice in Japan. We thought that a nation where white rice is a primary food would be receptive to using wild rice in their diet. To gain access to the food editors of Food Magazines, mainly based out of New York, we contracted with Howard Helmer to represent the wild rice industry. He was contracted to represent the egg industry and had obtained the Guinness Book of World Records for making the most egg omelets in one hour. Howard had a personality and style of making presentations that captured the attention of the listeners. The Wild Rice Council arranged for tours of the industry, and Howard Helmer arranged for prominent food editors to come to Minnesota for a 3-day tour. The tour consisted of a bus tour of growing, processing, and dining at special restaurants featuring wild rice dishes (soup, salad, main dishes, and desserts). The last day of the tour was a "highlight" where the food editors were given a "hands on" demonstration of cooking wild rice in the "teaching" kitchen (with several cooking stations) of Food Editor, Bea Ojakangas, in Duluth, Minnesota. Bea has published wild rice cookbooks and has great knowledge of the nutritional and taste benefits in recipes using wild rice. Food Editors who made one of the three tours given wrote articles and food recipes in magazines and newspapers, such as: Woman's Day, Food and Wine, Parade, Sunset, Food Communications Family Weekly, Farm & Ranch, magazines; and Chicago, New York, St. Paul, Atlanta newspapers, etc.

When George retired due to failing health, his secretary,

Nancy Tetrick, filled in until the appointment of Claude Titus. Claude had retired as the head of the Chamber of Commerce in Grand Rapids. The office was moved from Aitkin to Grand Rapids above the Norwest Bank, and Marge Wilson, who had been Claude's secretary at the Chamber, was hired as secretary. We were always thinking of new ways to promote wild rice, and I had the thought that Minnesota has a State flower, fish, bird, tree, etc., but no State grain. These appear on the State map and other State publications at no cost. As travelers enter the State, they are offered the free State map and other promotional materials. So why not get this free promotion for wild rice. I requested our State Senator and House Representative to draw up and introduce a bill naming wild rice as the Minnesota State Grain. There was some opposition from the corn growers because Minnesota has many acres and is a large producer of corn, but corn came from Central America. The fact was that wild rice is the only cereal grain that was here in the wild before the white man came to our State and Nation. Wild rice can claim the title of being the ONLY grain transferred from a native wild crop to a farm-grown agricultural crop in our Nation. After our testifying and pointing out this fact, in 1977 it was approved in the State House and Senate, and signed by Governor Rudy Perpich, a native from Hibbing, to be MINNESOTA'S STATE GRAIN. This has proven to me how a "thought" of a plain citizen can become a significant, long-lasting and important event for an industry and the economy.

In the mid-1980's, when Claude Titus was the Executive Director of the Wild Rice Council, we had the idea that we would get some good publicity by presenting wild rice to the President of the United States, Ronald Reagan. We now had a Republican Senator, Rudy Boschwitz, who should be able to arrange for this to happen. A letter of request stating our efforts to promote a new food crop and desire to present it to the President was sent to Senator Boschwitz. Our Senator went to work on this request, and one day our Council office received a call from the Senator's office telling us our request had been granted. Claude and I, along with R. Tretsvan and wife from the Minnesota Department of Agriculture, were to join Senator Boschwitz two days later to meet President Reagan at 3:00 p.m. in the White House. We hurriedly made the travel arrangements to fly out of the Twin Cities early that morning and to return the same evening. It would make for a long day, but we were fired up with adrenaline with the realization that we were going to meet the President of the United States. We caught a cab to the Senator's office. When the time came to go to the White House for our meeting, Senator Boschwitz drove us in his personal car. It was easy for us to get through the gate to the White House in the Senator's car, with a salute and greeting to the Senator. The same was true in passing the U. S. Marine guard at the door to the White House. We were ushered into the meeting room, with the huge oval table where the President and his appointed leaders meet, to await our assigned meeting time with the President. We were awed by the sights from this room--the table itself with the large chairs where so many important issues are discussed, and the White House lawn outside of this room where the staff was setting up tables in preparation for an important luncheon. On exactly the designated time, we were ushered into the adjoining Oval Office for a 5-minute meeting with President Reagan. We were introduced to the President and received a friendly, firm, cowboy-like handshake. See Pic. 19. We had exactly 5 minutes to tell our story about wild rice, to present the President with a gift of wild rice, and to suggest that he ask his chef to prepare a dish for him. We received a letter later that they had served wild rice for a luncheon for special guests. After our meeting it was time to return to the Senate Building and get ready for our evening flight home.

Senator Boschwitz showed us the sites of Washington, D. C., and was so intent on showing us around that as he approached the Capitol area he was going the wrong way on a one-way street. His comment to us when he discovered the error was, "Oh well! A Senator has the right to do that in Washington, D. C." So we continued until he got to his parking spot. This meeting of a U. S. President was a thrill of a lifetime. President Reagan made us feel welcome and gave us "hicks from the sticks" his undivided attention for five minutes.

Pic. 19 Pres. R. Reagan, Sen. R. Boschwitz,
R. Tretsvan, H. Kosbau, C. Titus

When Senator Boschwitz, a republican, ran for re-election, he was defeated by Paul Wellstone, a democrat. Senator Wellstone was a freshman in the Senate, and did not know the people in the Department of Agriculture nor the President and his staff. He had been a college professor of government and history and was not familiar with the wild rice industry. Thus, our relationship and educational efforts with this Senatorial seat was back to ground zero.

Ron Nelson became the Executive Director of the Minnesota Wild Rice Council after Claude Titus retired. Ron had graduated from the University of Minnesota in Ag. Economics and was well qualified for this position. His tenure was short due to an ailment which caused his death.

Beth Nelson had been the Executive Director for the Minnesota Egg Council and worked for the Minnesota Turkey Council. She had an office in the Twin Cities and arrangements were made with her to assume the responsibilities of Executive Director. There were advantages for the Minnesota paddy wild rice industry to contract with Beth, as follows: 1) Experience in promoting Minnesota agricultural products. 2) Acquaintances in the other ag. councils, Department of Agriculture, University of Minnesota Agricultural Research, and the Media; 3) Experience with promoting products at Trade Shows and the State Fair; 4) and, most important, an office close to all these activities. These professional values that Beth brought to the wild rice industry have been very beneficial to a new agricultural crop. Her efforts for the industry have helped tremendously to open doors to the food industry by her employing educated food economists to develop new uses and recipes, print new recipe booklets to hand out at the State Fair along with demonstrations of cooking wild rice, and developing articles for the food publications. Beth has vigilantly kept in contact with the State and Federal Legislators about the concerns of the paddy wild rice industry for research, favorable regulations, and awareness of the importance of this new agricultural crop.

# Growing Pains and Progress of a New Crop

The development of the major farm crops grown today have been changed from wild to domestic over centuries of time. When they were first taken from the wild and transferred to being grown by people, it was done on a very small scale. Improvements in the crop for increases, new varieties with different qualities, higher yields, disease resistance, etc. were developed over many years and even centuries. With wild rice it was different because it was being domesticated in the 1950-60's, 20th Century--the high technology, jet-speed age. Our World has shrunk and everything is being done on a "We want it now" basis. The "taming of wild rice" was done in less than 50 years. However, there are still many advancements to be made, just like there are on all of the other crops. Probably more in wild rice because it is still a relatively small crop and does not have the public interest, financial backing, nor the amount of research support that goes in to the major crops.

Adventurous people with ideas and fortitude to carry them out are the people who deserve credit for changing wild rice from a "wild" crop to a farm-grown "domestic" crop. This would never have happened if "possibility thinkers", had not put their thoughts into actions.

The real pioneers of this new industry are those who stepped out first and invested their ideas and money in a risky adventure. The people who stand out in my mind are as follows: Franklin Kosbau, who made the first machine to successfully harvest shattering wild rice, harnessed the air-boat to quickly and efficiently thin wild rice, discovered that wild rice does not need to mature in standing water, developed a mechanized way of turning and curing wild rice, and developed the K-2 variety as the first high-quality, non-shattering wild rice. Algot Johnson, who developed the first strain of non- shattering wild rice to be harvested with a farm combine. Erwin Brooks, a plant breeder who researched and developed some of the early new varieties of wild rice. Clifton Nelson, a pioneer in processing and marketing wild rice. Uncle Ben's Inc., who was one of the first major food companies to incorporate wild rice with white rice and launch a Nation-wide marketing campaign to sell the product. University of Minnesota Department Heads, like Dr. Hueg; Research Station Heads, like Dr. Matalmaki; Research Professors in the fields of Agriculture Plant Breeding, Plant Genetics, Entomology, Agricultural Engineering, Plant Pathology, Soil Science, Agronomy, and Food Science--names too numerous to mention.

Wild rice has many benefits to our World as a new domestic crop. The benefits that I can think of are as follows: 1) Highly nutritious grain featuring the values needed for a healthy diet--low fat, high protein, high fiber, and high in phosphorus and potassium. 2) Produced on flat, mainly organic soils in Minnesota that had been difficult to grow other farm crops on and had been non-productive land in the Northern Counties. The millions of acres of peat lands in Northern Minnesota had not produced much income for the Counties and Townships causing them to be poor and require assistance for all of the services provided to the residents. 3) New cereal grain for a World that is short of enough food to feed all of the people. 4) New money for the economy from jobs, new services needed for a new growing industry, purchases from local merchants, new industry businesses for processing and marketing, and an increase in the prices of rural land that had very little resale value 5) Potential for growth and expansion to other States and Countries.

Wildlife has been a significant benefactor of the controlled wetlands created by man-made wild rice paddies. Ducks and geese in particular benefit from the abundance of water and food as a resting place during the north and south migrations. Many of them stay and nest on the high, dry dikes with good grass cover. Floods will never destroy the nests and there is water nearby for the young on which to get their lessons of swimming and eating. Two studies have been done by graduate students at the University of North Dakota, which conclude that wild rice paddies are better than the man-made waterfowl habitat improvements. Pic. 20 was taken by Hal of swans and geese resting and feeding in a spring migration on our paddies at Aitkin, Minnesota.

Pic. 20: Swans and geese rest and feed in Aitkin, Minnesota. (Photo by Hal Kosbau)

Pic. 21: Mother Teal and 12 babies enjoy the habitat

Animals that thrive around wild rice paddies who enjoy the minnows and shellfish that live in the warm paddy waters are raccoons, weasel, mink, otters and muskrats. The deer travel the dikes and enjoy the rich forage and the plentiful supply of water.

Pic. 22: Deer enjoy the rich forage and the plentiful supply of water

# Wild Rice Farming in pictures:

Pic. 23: Mallards landing to feed in wild rice field

Pic. 24: Geese resting on dikes of wild rice field

Pic. 25: Minnesota State Flower - moccasin - on wetlands adjoining
wild rice paddies

Pic. 26: Wild Rice paddies by Little Willow River.

Pic. 27: Wild Rice (K-2) in blossom

Pic. 28: Wild Rice being harvested

Pic. 29: Combine unloaded to truck for transport to processing plant

Pic. 30: Water pump to flood wild rice paddies

Pic. 31: Greg (right), J. Pratt (on tailgate with suspenders), Bradley (behind pickup) and other employees eating lunch provided by "chuckwagon"

Pic. 32: Greg on MF 750 combine

Pic. 33: Art unloading wild rice with dump wagon used to transport wild rice from combine to semi-trailer

Pic. 34: Township road next to paddies flooded by a 5" and a 6" rain in one week

Pic. 35: Paddies re-flooded by excessive rainfall making harvest very difficult.

Pic.36: Wild rice plants have head on top of plant and pollen below the seed. Height is 5 – 8 feet.

# Inside the Deerwood Rice & Grain Processing plant:

Pic. 37: Harold and Betty talk about function of "dryers" to food editors.

Pic. 38: After drying, wild rice goes to rubber-roll "hullers" to remove hulls. Harold checking output.

Pic. 39: From "huller" to "indent separator" to separate broken from whole kernels.

Pic. 40: Last to "gravity" to separate unhulled from clean whole grain. Rice is then bagged and placed on pallets.

Pic. 41: Harold shows food editors the warehouse where wild rice is stored

# The Future for Wild Rice looks great!

Pic. 42: Joe, Jena and Nathan playing wild rice harvesting on Grandparents' shag carpeting.

# Favorite
# Wild Rice Recipes

## COOKING WILD RICE THE EASY WAY

Put 7 cups water in large sauce pan. Add 1 lb. Wild Rice and 2 tsp. salt. Bring to a boil. Turn down heat, cover and continue to cook at a slow boil for 20 to 25 minutes. Let stand covered for at least 3 to 4 hours, or overnight. Drain any excess liquid. This makes 11 cups of cooked wild rice.
Store what you are not going to use in freezer bags (say 2 or 3 cups) and freeze. Now you have instant wild rice to use.

Here are some hints for using the precooked wild rice:

1. Add to uncooked meat in hamburgers or meatloaf. It holds the moisture and adds taste.
2. Mix in with scrambled eggs or in an omelet.
3. Sprinkle on pancakes to add taste and texture.
4. Add to favorite soups, casseroles, salads and desserts.


## BETTY'S EASY WILD RICE SOUP

5 cups precooked wild rice
1 can evaporated milk
1 pkg. cheese (from Mac & Cheese Box)
1 pkg. dried onion soup mix
1 pound ham, cubed
1 cup celery, chopped
1 cup onion, chopped
1/2 green pepper, chopped

Sautee celery, onions, pepper and ham. Combine remaining ingredients and simmer 15 minutes or more. Serve and enjoy.


## BETTY'S WILD RICE CASSEROLE

4 to 5 cups precooked wild rice
1 lb. hamburger
3 slices bacon, chopped
1/2 cup celery, chopped
1/2 cup onion, chopped
1/4 cup green pepper, chopped

99

1/2 pkg. onion soup mix
1--4 oz. can mushrooms
1 can cream chicken soup
3 tablespoons sour cream

Brown hamburger and bacon. Add onions, celery, green pepper, mushrooms, dried and liquid soup. Add 1 cup water, sour cream and wild rice.
Bake for 40 to 45 minutes in microwave. Top with grated cheese.
Husband is taste tester and wife gets all the praise.


## BETTY'S WILD RICE FRUIT SALAD

4 cups precooked wild rice
1 med. can cubed pineapple, drained
1 apple, chopped
1 can mandarin oranges, drained (regular oranges can be used)
1/2 to 1 cup walnuts or pecans, chopped
1 banana, chopped
1/2 cup coconut, optional
1 tablespoon maple flavoring
2 cups miniature marshmallows
Fresh peaches, grapes and nectarines are great additions
Mix in one 6 ounce can frozen orange juice

Marinate in refrigerator 1 hour or more. Hide from husband or it will disappear.


## BETTY'S WILD RICE ICE CREAM TOPPING

1 cup precooked wild rice
1 cup brown sugar
1 cup nuts, chopped
½ cup dates (optional)
1/4 cup white syrup
½ stick butter or margarine
½ cup maraschino cherries, chopped
1 tsp. maple flavoring
½ cup water
1/4 tsp. salt

Combine brown sugar, butter and water.  Bring slowly to boil and stir in white syrup. Continue stirring frequently during boil until a little dropped into cold water forms a soft ball.  Add cherries, nuts, dates and salt.  Cook until it thickens a little.  Add wild rice to sauce and serve warm over ice cream.  Note: Don't add wild rice until just ready to serve or kernels will harden.


## HAL'S WILD RICE 'DREAM CAKE'

2 cups precooked wild rice
2 cups apples, chopped
1 cup brown sugar
1 cup white sugar
½ cup butter or oleo
2 tsp. caramel or maple flavoring
1 tsp. cinnamon
½ tsp. nutmeg
¼ tsp. salt
2 eggs, beaten
1 ½ cups four
2 tsp. baking soda
1 cup nuts, chopped

Blend sugars, butter, flour, soda with beaten eggs. Add flavoring, spices, salt, wild rice, and apples, mix well. Stir in chopped nuts. Pour in baking pan and bake for 30 minutes at 350 degrees. Serve with whipped topping or ice cream. "Memories of Hal."

# Notes / Recipes

# Notes / Recipes

# Notes / Recipes

# Notes / Recipes